This Pokémon Annual belongs to:

....

....

Age: ....

My Pokémon Buddy is:

....

EGMONT

We bring stories to life

First published in Great Britain in 2019
by Egmont UK Limited
The Yellow Building, 1 Nicholas Road, London W11 4AN

ISBN 978 1 4052 9440 9
70376/004
Printed in Italy

Written and designed by Cloud King Creative.

A CIP catalogue record for this book is available from the British Library.

Stay safe online. Egmont is not responsible for content hosted by third parties.

Egmont takes its responsibility to the planet and its inhabitants very seriously.
We aim to use papers from well-managed forests run by responsible suppliers.

Pokémon™

Annual 2020

Contents

Ready for Adventure!

Join Ash, Pikachu and their friends for more exciting adventures in the tropical Alola region! Ash has his own Z-Ring and can now perform Z-Moves in battle! He's met so many more new Pokémon on his travels and during his studies at the Pokémon School, too.

In this book, you can read stories about Ash's quest to become a Pokémon Master and learn about new Pokémon in the Alolan A–Z. Plus, complete the special island challenges to earn your own Z-Ring, just like Ash!

Friends 'til the end!

Teaming Up

Ash's friends are more than just classmates, together they form the Ultra Guardians – a team tasked by Lusamine with finding and capturing Ultra Beast invaders in the Alola region.

Kiawe

Pokémon: Turtonator, Alolan Marowak, Charizard (Ride Pokémon)

Fiery and determined, Kiawe is serious about everything he does, whether it's battling, or working on his family's farm. He lives with his parents and his little sister, Mimo, on Akala Island. Kiawe inherited his grandfather's Charizard, who now carries him to school and helps him with deliveries. He also has a Z-Ring, which was given to him by Kahuna Olivia.

Lana

Pokémon: Popplio, Nagisa, Dragonair (Ride Pokémon)

A quiet girl with a mischievous streak, Lana is an expert fisher and loves everything about the sea. She takes care of her younger sisters, twins Harper and Sarah, and her partner Popplio, whom she rescued from some bullies on the beach. She also has a Z-Ring.

Lillie

Pokémon: Alolan Vulpix, Altaria (Ride Pokémon)

The sheltered Lillie grew up in a rich family, including her older brother Gladion – but rather than being stuck-up or snobby, she's polite and kind. Lillie knows a lot about Pokémon and sometimes sounds like a Pokédex when she talks about them – but she avoids touching Pokémon other than her partner, an Alolan Vulpix named Snowy.

Mallow

Pokémon: A Tsareena that evolved from a Bounsweet and a Steenee, Flygon (Ride Pokémon)

Mallow has a cheerful and energetic personality, but she tends to jump to conclusions. She's good friends with Lana and Lillie. When she's not with her classmates, she helps her father, Abe, run their family restaurant – she's a good cook as well as an awesome athlete.

Sophocles

Pokémon: Togedemaru, Charjabug, Metang (Ride Pokémon)

An electronics genius and an expert computer programmer, Sophocles tends to throw himself into anything he finds interesting. He's curious about Rotom Dex and really wants to take it apart to see what makes it tick.

Meet Gladion

Lillie's older brother and Ash's rival, Gladion, may come across as gloomy, but he's a talented Trainer who is both loyal and fearless.

Brave in Battle

Prone to brooding and outbursts of intense emotion, Gladion's impressive battling skills have driven off both Team Skull and Team Rocket and inspired Ash to seek out more Z-Crystals. Gladion is protective of his Pokémon partners, particularly the mysterious one who wears a mask.

Fact File

FAMILY:
Lusamine (mother),
Lillie (sister)
RIVALS:
Ash, Team Skull,
Team Rocket
TRAINER CLASS:
Pokémon Trainer
POKÉMON:
Umbreon,
Lycanroc (Midnight Form)

Special Stones

Mega Stones are special stones that allow particular Pokémon to evolve into their final form. Draw lines to connect the stones to the mega-evolved Pokémon.

Which Pokémon is missing its Mega Stone? Colour in the stone using the coloured dots to help it evolve.

MEGA SHARPEDO

SABLENITE

SCIZORITE

PINSIRITE

MEGA PINSIR

GENGARITE

EGA SABLEYE

SHARPEDONITE

ABSOLITE

MEGA GYARADOS

GYARADOSITE

MEGA SCIZOR

MEGA GENGAR

The answers are on page 69.

11

Pokémon Partners

There are some truly amazing creatures in Alola! Work out which Pokémon makes the perfect partner for Ash and each of his friends.

Write the name of the Trainer next to their Pokémon pal.

MALLOW
❯ My pal is a Grass-type Pokémon.
❯ Its long legs can deliver powerful kicks in battle.
❯ It's known for its beautiful appearance.
❯ It evolved from a Steenee.

ASH
❯ My Pokémon is pretty electric!
❯ It even stores electric energy in its cheeks.
❯ We've had so many awesome adventures together.
❯ Its tail is shaped like a lightning bolt.

LANA
❯ My Pokémon is a perfect Water-type.
❯ We are both expert swimmers!
❯ In battle, it can fire water balloons against a foe.
❯ Its smooth skin is as blue as the ocean.

TSAREENA

....

POPPLIO

....

ALOLAN VULPIX

....

KIAWE

》 My buddy is a Fire- and Dragon- type.
》 It stands tall, at two metres high.
》 It can spew flames and poisonous gases from its nostrils.
》 The shell on its back can explode when struck in battle.

LILLIE

》 Some people in the Alola region know this Pokémon as "Keokeo".
》 Its fur is as white as snow.
》 It has six tails that can spray out ice crystals.
》 It loves cold environments, as it's an Ice-type Pokémon.

PIKACHU

· · · · · · · · · · · · · · ·

TURTONATOR

· · · · · · · · · · · · · · ·

The answers are on page 69.

Island Challenge: Melemele Island

Melemele Island was where Ash's adventures in the Alola region first began. He loved it so much that he enrolled at the Pokémon School there! Try your hand at these Alolan activities.

Find **five** Pokémon hiding in this scene. Tick each one as you find it.

Gumshoos ⬡ **Alolan Raticate** ⬡ **Wishiwashi** ⬡

Poipole ⬡ **Tapu Koko** ⬡

Forest Friend

Join the dots to reveal the island's curious Electric- and Fairy-type Pokémon.

1

41
43
50   2
9
11

44
42
49   8
3   10
48   4   5   13
47   6   12
46   19 18
39   34 33   7
40

45   32   20
35   31   17
30   21
22   14
38   15
37

28   24

36   16

29   23
27   25

26

The answers are on page 69.

Guiding an Awakening

Ash and his Pokémon have landed on the Alolan island of Ula'ula, for Ash's next grand trial. He'll be challenging Nanu, the island Kahuna, in a trial that's set to be Ash's toughest test yet …

Everyone had gathered at the Island Ruins for the trial to begin.

"The grand trial is part of the Ula'ula Island challenge," said Nanu, clutching the crystal around his neck. "To pass, you must defeat all three of my Pokémon. But here's the catch … you must do it with only one Pokémon."

Ash gasped, **"One Pokémon?"**

"That doesn't seem fair," bleeped Rotom Dex.

"Uncle Nanu's trial will test whether a Trainer can overcome adversity," Acerola explained. Nanu's niece was going to play referee.

Ash had to choose his strongest Pokémon. Was Lycanroc tough enough to take on Nanu's three?

"Are you up for this?" he asked Lycanroc.

Lycanroc let out a determined growl.

"Then we accept!" Ash said firmly.

"I was sure you'd give up when you heard about my three-on-one," teased Nanu. "I hope you trained."

"Of course we trained!" Ash replied.

"Then **off we go!**" said Nanu.

"The challenger, Ash, from Pallet Town, versus Nanu, Kahuna of Ula'ula Island," Acerola announced. **"Battle begins!"**

Nanu launched his first Poké Ball. Out jumped Krookodile, unleashing a mighty **"KROOKA!"**

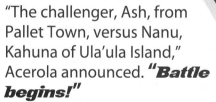

Krookodile had defeated Lycanroc once before, but Ash wasn't worried – Lycanroc had grown up a lot since then.

Nanu made the first move. "Krookodile: *Mud Slap!*"

Lycanroc dodged it, but Krookodile used *Sand Tomb* next, landing Lycanroc in a pit of sinking sand! Lycanroc quickly leapt free, shaking the sand from its mane, as its eyes glowed red.

"Way to go, Lycanroc!" smiled Ash. "Now, use *Rock Throw!*"

Lycanroc launched hundreds of flying rocks, but Krookodile swished them away with its tail.

Nanu sneered. "Can't you see it's useless? To win a Pokémon battle you must use your best attack." he advised.

Ash realised that to beat Krookodile he had to get closer, but was Lycanroc ready to try a new move?

Lycanroc growled to Ash – the Pokémon *was* ready … and had a new move that might just work.

"I hear you!" smiled Ash. "Use *Accelerock!*"

This time, the move was just too powerful for Krookodile. The Darkness Pokémon fell to the floor.

"*Lycanroc wins!*" Acerola declared.

"*You did it!*" Ash hugged Lycanroc.

One battle down! Next up was Sableye, who opened with *Shadow Ball*. Ash and Lycanroc countered with *Rock Throw*.

"*Mean Look!*" Nanu commanded next, which froze Lycanroc to the spot. Sableye struck again, with *Shadow Claw*.

Lycanroc's eyes glowed red again. "*Stay calm!*" Ash shouted. He had to think fast. Sableye was too far away to try *Bite*. *Rock Throw* wouldn't work either. "Use *Stone Edge!*" he cried.

Nanu gasped, as Lycanroc slammed down his paws, causing the ground in front of him to crack. A huge stone mound appeared, trapping Sableye.

"**Way to go!**" Ash cheered.

"Sableye is unable to battle," called Acerola. "**Lycanroc wins!**"

One more win and Ash would pass the grand trial! But Lycanroc was looking tired … would it survive another battle?

Just then, everyone looked up, as a dark shape appeared overhead. It was **Tapu Bulu**! Ula'ula's island guardian dropped a berry for Ash to catch.

"Sitrus Berries restore a Pokémon's strength," Rotom Dex explained.

Ash fed it to Lycanroc, who gladly accepted the island guardian's gift.

Ash and Lycanroc's final opponent was an Alolan Persian. It began the battle with **Power Gem**, blasting a stream of blue light from the jewel on its forehead. The move sent Lycanroc tumbling – Ash had to counter quickly.

"Use **Stone Edge**," he said, when Lycanroc had recovered The move worked! Persian was hit, but it wasn't defeated.

"You really **have** been training," smiled Nanu. "Though Lycanroc would be just fine without you."

"What do you mean?" said Ash, through gritted teeth.

"Lycanroc would get even stronger without you …" said Nanu. "A Pokémon should choose the Trainer who's best suited to them."

Ash's cheeks burned red. "Are you saying I'm not?" he growled. "We've been together ever since it was a Rockruff. It even **evolved**."

Nanu's plan was working … Ash's rising temper was making him lose focus. The Island Kahuna quickly launched his next move. "Persian, use **Dark Pulse**!"

Ash was slow to react. "Shake it off!" he called to Lycanroc.

Lycanroc roared and broke free from the Persian's attack. It fought back with *Accelerock*, but Persian used *Dark Pulse* again.

Ash was puzzled. "Why do you keep using the same move?" he asked Nanu.

"I like the look in its eyes – *see for yourself*!" Nanu replied.

As Ash approached Lycanroc, its eyes glowed a deep red with rage. Nanu had deliberately tried to make Lycanroc mad, just as he had done to Ash, to distract him!

"Self-destructing, just as I planned!" Nanu laughed.

"We'll never do that!" Ash shouted furiously.

But Lycanroc was *out of control*! When Ash tried to make his Pokémon calm down, Lycanroc turned on him, knocking him off his feet.

"Lycanroc! That's Ash!" cried Rotom Dex.

Ash sat up, clutching his side. He looked into Lycanroc's red eyes. This time, he understood what was happening. "Anger isn't turning your eyes red …" Ash smiled. *"You're boosting your power!"*

"Ruff!" growled Lycanroc.

"That tackle was the wake-up call I needed," said Ash.

"Lycanroc can keep its cool, even when its eyes go bright red! Data update complete!" buzzed Rotom Dex.

"Back to the battle!" said Ash.
Nanu shrugged. He'd thought the trial was over.

"Prepare to lose!" he warned. "Multiple **Night Slashes!**"
Persian swiped at Lycanroc, delivering blow after blow, but Lycanroc stood firm. The two Pokémon leapt into the air together, before Lycanroc struck first, in a move that Ash had never seen.

"Yes!" smiled Ash. "You used **Counter**."

Nanu had to up the stakes. "Never thought I'd have to use this," he said. He took the dark crystal from around his neck and clicked it into his Z-Ring. The **Darkinium Z-Crystal** would allow Persian to perform an incredible Z-Move!

"Use **Black Hole Eclipse**," Nanu told his Pokémon.

The sky turned black – Ash had to act fast. "A Z-Move for a Z-Move …" he said. **"Continental CRUSH!"**

Lycanroc launched an enormous boulder to quickly smother Persian's eclipse.

"Lycanroc's Z-Move cancelled out the other Z-Move!" Rotom Dex bleeped.

With Persian stunned, Ash and Lycanroc used **Accelerock** to defeat Nanu's third Pokémon at last.

"Persian is unable to battle!" Acerola announced. "Three wins give Ash and Lycanroc the victory!"

"We won!" laughed Ash.

"Well done, kid," said Nanu nobly. "You've earned a Dark-type **Z-Crystal**. But … you're not suited to the dark, are you?"

Ash's jaw dropped. Were all his efforts about to go to waste?

"Take this instead," said Nanu, handing him a small brown crystal. "**A Lycanium Z**. It can only be used to launch a Z-Move with Lycanroc."

Ash had never seen a crystal like it before. "Wow, for me?" he smiled.

With the trial complete, soon it was time to head back to Melemele Island.

"Come again soon, Ash," said Acerola.

"Visit us at the Pokémon School, too," Ash smiled back.

As Ula'ula port disappeared into the distance, Ash talked to his Pokémon. "Let's keep getting stronger … and pass the next grand trial!" He was determined to be the very best Trainer he could be.

"PIKA!" squeaked Pikachu proudly.

Ash *and his Pokémon have passed their third grand trial with three wins. Now, with the Lycanium Z, find out what adventures lie in store, as the journey continues on* **page 50***.*

Island Challenge: Akala Island

Akala Island was the second island that Ash visited in the Alola region. Challenge yourself with these Pokémon puzzles from Akala.

Akala Island is home to Kiawe and all these Pokémon! Find their names – plus Ash and Pikachu's – in the word puzzle below. The words read forwards, backwards, up, down and diagonally.

Word list:
- ASH
- PIKACHU
- KIAWE
- TAPU LELE
- PYUKUMUKU
- YUNGOOS
- COMFEY
- ORANGURU
- STUFFUL
- ALOLAN MAROWAK
- SANDYGAST
- PIKIPEK

U	G	N	H	S	T	U	F	F	U	L	K	M	U	W
Z	T	C	C	U	J	D	R	H	W	Q	T	S	T	R
W	A	L	O	L	A	N	M	A	R	O	W	A	K	B
R	L	A	L	M	W	C	J	K	S	T	L	N	I	Y
E	J	Q	R	B	F	M	D	M	B	H	G	D	A	N
S	U	G	R	T	K	E	S	Y	C	O	J	Y	W	T
M	C	T	P	D	P	G	Y	N	Z	R	B	G	X	E
B	H	Z	I	S	Q	I	T	G	R	A	Q	A	H	L
P	Y	U	K	U	M	U	K	U	L	N	C	S	M	E
C	U	B	A	L	U	B	I	I	H	G	L	T	C	L
T	N	M	C	Z	J	S	A	W	P	E	U	W	Q	U
Y	G	P	H	K	H	K	W	L	Q	E	G	M	Z	P
U	O	T	U	C	Q	J	E	U	S	N	K	K	R	A
Q	O	P	W	J	Z	B	T	W	H	P	B	H	G	T
A	S	K	G	O	R	A	N	G	U	R	U	Z	U	V

ISLAND KAHUNA

Now rearrange the shaded letters in grey to reveal the name of the Island Kahuna. Is it:

NANU ⬡ HALU ⬡ OLIVIA ⬡ HAPU ⬡

Hungry Pokémon

Follow the lines to work out which Pokémon from Akala is snacking on which juicy berry! Then find the Pokémon that will go hungry!

Pikipek

Yungoos

Oranguru

Pikachu

Alolan Marowak

Oran Berry

Pecha Berry

Sitrus Berry

Tamato Berry

The answers are on page 69.

Right Ring

Ash was given his Z-Ring as a gift from Tapu Koko, the Guardian of Melemele Island! Only one ring is the true Z-Ring – circle it.

A

B

C

D

E

The **Z-Ring** holds a **Z-Crystal**. Once in place, it allows Ash to perform **Z-Moves**!

The answers are on page 69.

Alolan »» A-Z

Ash and his friends have travelled far and wide across the tropical Alola region, meeting plenty of puzzling Pokémon and fascinating Ultra Beasts along the way. How many of these mysterious creatures do you know?

Araquanid

Type:
Water – Bug
Height & weight:
1.8 m/82.0 kg

About: In battle, Araquanid uses the water bubble that surrounds its head as a weapon, headbutting its opponents or cutting off their air. When it's not battling, it uses the bubble as a shield to protect its weaker companions.

Bewear

Type:
Normal – Fighting
Height & weight:
2.1 m/135.0 kg

About: Think twice before making friends with a Bewear. This super-strong Pokémon might be even more dangerous to those it likes, because it tends to deliver bone-crushing hugs as a sign of affection. Beware!

Blacephalon

Ultra Beast
Type:
Fire – Ghost
Height & weight:
1.8m/13.0kg

About: Blacephalon, one of the mysterious Ultra Beasts, has an unexpected method of attack: it makes its own head blow up! Its opponents are so surprised by this that it can take advantage and steal their energy.

Bounsweet

Type:
Grass
Height & weight:
0.3 m/3.2 kg

About: Bounsweet smells good enough to eat – which sometimes gets it into trouble! The intensely sugary liquid it gives off can be diluted to bring the sweetness level down so people can drink it.

Brionne

Type:
Water

Height & weight:
0.6 m/17.5 kg

About: Brionne pelts its opponents with water balloons in a swift and skilful battle dance. It also shows off its dancing abilities when trying to cheer up its Trainer.

Bruxish

Type:
Water – Psychic

Height & weight:
0.9 m/19.0 kg

About: Don't let the beguiling grin of the brightly coloured Bruxish fool you – those teeth are strong and sharp, and it can wield psychic powers mighty enough to stun an opponent in battle.

Buzzwole

Ultra Beast

Type:
Bug – Fighting

Height & weight:
2.4 m/333.6 kg

About: Buzzwole, one of the mysterious Ultra Beasts, is enormously strong, capable of demolishing heavy machinery with a punch. When it displays its impressive muscles, no one is sure whether it's just showing off – or issuing a threat.

Celesteela

Ultra Beast

Type:
Steel – Flying

Height & weight:
9.2 m/999.9 kg

About: Celesteela, one of the mysterious Ultra Beasts, can shoot incendiary gases from its arms and has been known to burn down wide swaths of trees. In flight, it can reach impressive speeds.

Charjabug

Type:
Bug – Electric

Height & weight:
0.5 m/10.5 kg

About: When Charjabug breaks down food for energy, some of that energy is stored as electricity inside its body. A Trainer who likes to go camping would appreciate having this Pokémon as a partner!

Comfey

Type:
Fairy

Height & weight:
0.1 m/0.3 kg

About: Comfey collects flowers and attaches them to its vine, where they flourish and release a calming fragrance. Adding these flowers to bathwater makes for a relaxing soak.

Cosmoem

Type:
Psychic

Height & weight:
0.1 m/999.9 kg

About: Cosmoem never moves, radiating a gentle warmth as it develops inside the hard shell that surrounds it. Long ago, people referred to it as the cocoon of the stars, and some still think its origins lie in another world.

Cosmog

Type:
Psychic

Height & weight:
0.2 m/0.1 kg

About: Cosmog reportedly came to the Alola region from another world, but its origins are shrouded in mystery. Known as the child of the stars, it grows by gathering dust from the atmosphere.

Crabominable

Type:
Fighting – Ice

Height & weight:
1.7 m/180.0 kg

About: Covered in warm fur, Crabominable evolved from Crabrawler that took their goal of aiming for the top a bit too literally and found themselves at the summit of icy mountains. They can detach their pincers and fling them at foes.

Crabrawler

Type:
Fighting

Height & weight:
0.6 m/7.0 kg

About: Crabrawler is always looking for a fight, and it really hates to lose. Sometimes its pincers come right off because it uses them for punching so much! Fortunately, it can regrow them quickly.

Cutiefly

Type:
Bug – Fairy

Height & weight:
0.1 m/0.2 kg

About: Cutiefly can sense the aura of flowers and gauge when they're ready to bloom, so it always knows where to find fresh nectar. If you notice a swarm of these Pokémon following you around, you might have a floral aura!

Dartrix

Type:
Grass – Flying

Height & weight:
0.7 m/16.0 kg

About: Dartrix is very conscious of its appearance and spends a lot of time keeping its wings clean. It can throw sharp-edged feathers, known as blade quills, with great accuracy.

Decidueye

Type:
Grass – Ghost

Height & weight:
1.6 m/36.6 kg

About: A natural marksman, Decidueye can shoot its arrow quills with astonishing precision, hitting a tiny target a hundred yards away. It tends to be calm and collected, but sometimes panics if it's caught off guard.

Dewpider

Type:
Water – Bug

Height & weight:
0.3 m/4.0 kg

About: Mostly aquatic, Dewpider brings a water-bubble 'helmet' along when it ventures onto the land to look for food. The bubble also lends extra power when it headbutts an opponent.

Dhelmise

Type:
Ghost – Grass

Height & weight:
3.9 m/210.0 kg

About: When Dhelmise swings its mighty anchor, even the biggest Pokémon have to watch out! It snags seaweed floating past on the waves and scavenges detritus from the seafloor to add to its body.

Alolan Diglett

Type:
Ground – Steel

Height & weight:
0.2 m/1.0 kg

About: The metal hairs that sprout from the top of Diglett's head can be used to communicate or to sense its surroundings. It can extend just those hairs above ground to make sure everything is safe before emerging.

Drampa

Type:
Normal – Dragon

Height & weight:
3.0 m/185.0 kg

About: Even wild Drampa have a real soft spot for kids. Though they make their home far away in the mountains, they often come into town to visit and play with the local children.

Alolan Dugtrio

Type:
Ground – Steel

Height & weight:
0.7 m/66.6 kg

About: Although Dugtrio's golden hair is shiny and beautiful, people aren't inclined to collect it when it falls – there are stories that doing so will bring bad luck. In Alola, this Pokémon is thought to represent the spirit of the land.

Alolan Exeggutor

Type:
Grass – Dragon

Height & weight:
10.9 m/415.6 kg

About: In the tropical sun and sand, Exeggutor grows exceptionally tall, unlocking draconic powers hidden deep within. Trainers in Alola are proud of the tree-like Exeggutor and consider this to be its ideal form.

Fomantis

Type:
Grass

Height & weight:
0.3 m/1.5 kg

About: Fomantis sleeps the day away, basking in the sunlight. The sweet scent it gives off sometimes attracts Cutiefly to its hiding place. During the night, it seeks out a safe place to sleep for the next day.

Alolan Geodude

Type:
Rock – Electric

Height & weight:
0.4 m/20.3 kg

About: In the Alola region, Geodude are naturally magnetic, and their bodies are often covered in iron particles they've picked up while sleeping in the sand. Stepping on one can cause a nasty shock, so beachgoers keep a sharp eye out.

Alolan Golem

Type:
Rock – Electric

Height & weight:
1.7 m/316.0 kg

About: The rocks Golem fires from its back carry a strong electrical charge, so even a glancing blow can deliver a powerful shock. Sometimes it grabs a Geodude to fire instead.

Golisopod

Type:
Bug – Water

Height & weight:
2.0 m/108.0 kg

About: When Golisopod has to battle, its six sharp-clawed arms are certainly up to the task. Most of the time, though, it lives quietly in underwater caves, where it meditates and avoids conflict.

Alolan Graveler

Type:
Rock – Electric

Height & weight:
1.0 m/110.0 kg

About: The crystals that appear on Graveler's body are the result of consuming dravite, a particularly tasty mineral. Graveler often fight over dravite deposits, crashing together with a sound like thunder.

Alolan Grimer

Type:
Poison – Dark

Height & weight:
0.7 m/42.0 kg

About: Grimer's appearance in the Alola region developed after it was called upon to deal with a persistent garbage problem. Each crystal on its body is formed from dangerous toxins, and those toxins escape if a crystal falls off.

Grubbin

Type:
Bug

Height & weight:
0.4 m/4.4 kg

About: Grubbin have discovered that sticking close to Electric-type Pokémon offers some protection from the Flying types that often like to attack them! With their strong jaws, they can scrape away tree bark to get at the delicious sap underneath.

Gumshoos

Type:
Normal

Height & weight:
0.7 m/14.2 kg

About: Gumshoos displays amazing patience when it's on a stakeout, waiting to ambush its prey. It's a natural enemy of Rattata, but the two rarely interact because they're awake at different times.

Guzzlord

Ultra Beast

Type:
Dark – Dragon

Height & weight:
5.5 m/888.0 kg

About: Guzzlord, one of the mysterious Ultra Beasts, seems to have an insatiable appetite for just about everything – it will even swallow buildings and mountains. This constant munching can be very destructive.

Hakamo-o

Type:
Dragon – Fighting

Height & weight:
1.2 m/47.0 kg

About: Hakamo-o regularly sheds its scales and grows new ones. Each set of scales is harder and sharper than the one before. It leaps at opponents with a battle cry, and the sharp scales turn its punches into a real threat.

Incineroar

Type:
Fire – Dark

Height & weight:
1.8 m/83.0 kg

About: Training an Incineroar requires patience – if it's not in just the right mood, it shows complete disregard for any orders given. During battle, it throws fierce punches and kicks, then launches the flames on its belly in a final attack.

Jangmo-o

Type:
Dragon
Height & weight:
0.6 m/29.7 kg

About: Wild Jangmo-o live in remote mountains, far away from people. When they smack their scales together, either in battle or to communicate, the mountains ring with the metallic sound.

Kartana

Ultra Beast
Type:
Grass – Steel
Height & weight:
0.3 m/0.1 kg

About: Kartana, one of the mysterious Ultra Beasts, can use its entire sharp-edged body as a weapon in battle. Its blade is strong and sharp enough to slice right through a steel structure in a single stroke.

Komala

Type:
Normal
Height & weight:
0.4 m/19.9 kg

About: Komala never wakes up – ever – although it does sometimes move around as it dreams. It lives in a permanent state of sleep, cuddling its precious log or its Trainer's arm.

Kommo-o

Type:
Dragon – Fighting
Height & weight:
1.6 m/78.2 kg

About: Long ago, Kommo-o scales were collected and turned into weapons. For this Pokémon, the scales provide offence, defence, and even a warning system – when it shakes its tail, the scales clash together in a jangle that scares off weak opponents.

Litten

Type:
Fire
Height & weight:
0.4 m/4.3 kg

About: When it grooms its fur, Litten is storing up ammunition – the flaming fur is later coughed up in a fiery attack. Trainers often have a hard time getting this solitary Pokémon to trust them.

Lunala

Type:
Psychic – Ghost
Height & weight:
4.0 m/120.0 kg

About: Lunala's wide wings soak up the light, turning bright days dark. Alola's largest Legendary Pokémon, it is said to make its home in another world, returning there when its third eye becomes active.

Lurantis

Type:
Grass

Height & weight:
0.9 m/18.5 kg

About: It can be difficult to give Lurantis the proper care to keep its colouring bright and vivid, but some Trainers enthusiastically accept the challenge. The beams it shoots from its petals can pierce thick metal.

Lycanroc Midday Form

Type:
Rock

Height & weight:
0.8 m/25.0 kg

About: Its thick mane conceals sharp rocks that it uses in battle along with its fangs and claws. Despite its fearsome arsenal, Lycanroc displays fierce loyalty toward a Trainer who has raised it well.

Lycanroc Dusk Form

Type:
Rock

Height & weight:
0.8 m/25.0 kg

About: Lycanroc's Dusk Form is a rare sight in Alola. It only appears when a Rockruff evolves at sunset, during the time between day and night. This Pokémon's calm demeanour hides a strong impulse to battle.

Lycanroc Midnight Form

Type:
Rock

Height & weight:
1.1 m/25.0 kg

About: When Lycanroc faces a truly intimidating opponent, it attacks recklessly, with no concern for its own hide. The rocks in its mane contribute to the crushing power of its headbutt.

Magearna

Type:
Steel – Fairy

Height & weight:
1.0 m/80.5 kg

About: Magearna was built many centuries ago by human inventors. The rest of this Pokémon's mechanical body is just a vehicle for its true self: the Soul-Heart contained in its chest.

Mareanie

Type:
Poison – Water

Height & weight:
0.4 m/8.0 kg

About: Mareanie lives at the bottom of the sea or along the beach. It attacks with its head spike, which delivers poison that can weaken a foe. It's often tempted by the brightly coloured coral of Corsola.

Alolan Marowak

Type:
Fire – Ghost

Height & weight:
1.0 m/34.0 kg

About: The flaming bone that Marowak spins like a baton once belonged to its mother, and it's protected by its mother's spirit. It grieves for its fallen companions, visiting their graves along the roadside.

Marshadow

Type:
Fighting – Ghost

Height & weight:
0.7 m/22.2 kg

About: Very few people have seen Marshadow, so it was considered a rumour. Always cowering in the shadows, it watches others closely and mimics their movements.

Alolan Meowth

Type:
Dark

Height & weight:
0.4 m/4.2 kg

About: Meowth is very vain about the golden Charm on its forehead, becoming enraged if any dirt dulls its bright surface. These crafty Pokémon are not native to Alola, but thanks to human interference, their population has surged.

Mimikyu

Type:
Ghost – Fairy

Height & weight:
0.2 m/0.7 kg

About: What does Mimikyu look like? No one really knows, but apparently it's terrifying – it always hides underneath an old rag so it doesn't scare anyone while it's trying to make friends.

Minior Meteor Form

Type:
Rock – Flying

Height & weight:
0.3 m/40.0 kg

About: Minior came into being when tiny particles in the ozone layer underwent mutation. When its shell becomes too heavy, it falls to the ground, and the impact can knock its shell clean off.

Minior Red Core

Type:
Rock – Flying

Height & weight:
0.3 m/0.3 kg

About: The atmospheric dust that Minior consumes influences the colour of its core. When the core is exposed, it's extremely vulnerable, and Trainers are advised to get it into a Poké Ball immediately for protection.

Morelull

Type:
Grass – Fairy
Height & weight:
0.2 m/1.5 kg

About: The spores that Morelull gives off flicker with a hypnotic light that sends viewers to sleep. During the day, it plants itself beside a tree to absorb nutrients from the roots while it naps.

Mudbray

Type:
Ground
Height & weight:
1.0 m/110.0 kg

About: Mudbray just loves to get dirty, but it isn't just for fun. Playing in the mud actually gives it better traction for running – when its hooves are covered in dirt, they're less likely to slip, and it can run faster.

Mudsdale

Type:
Ground
Height & weight:
2.5 m/920.0 kg

About: With the help of the mud that coats its hooves, Mudsdale can deliver heavy kicks powerful enough to demolish a big truck. The mud it produces is weather-resistant, and people used to use it to shore up their houses.

Alolan Muk

Type:
Poison – Dark
Height & weight:
1.0 m/52.0 kg

About: Muk's bright and colourful markings are the result of chemical changes in its body, caused by its diet of all sorts of garbage. It's generally a pleasant and friendly companion, but if it gets hungry, it can turn

Naganadel

Ultra Beast

Type:
Poison – Dragon
Height & weight:
3.6m/150.0kg

About: Naganadel, one of the mysterious Ultra Beasts, stores a poisonous liquid in vast quantities inside its body. The poison, which gives off an eerie glow and adheres to anything it touches, can be fired from its needles.

Necrozma

Type:
Psychic
Height & weight:
2.4 m/230.0 kg

About: Some think Necrozma arrived from another world many eons ago. When it emerges from its underground slumber, it seems to absorb light for use as energy to power its laser-like blasts.

Necrozma  Dawn Wings

Type:
Psychic – Ghost

Height & weight:
4.2m/350.0kg

About: When Necrozma absorbs Lunala's light and power, it takes on this form. Dawn Wings Necrozma gives off energy at a reckless pace as it rips at its opponents with its enormous claws.

Necrozma  Dusk Mane

Type:
Psychic – Steel

Height & weight:
3.8m/460.0kg

About: When Necrozma absorbs Solgaleo's light and power, it takes on this form. Dusk Mane Necrozma is uncontrollable and vicious, slashing at opponents with its many claws.

Ultra Necrozma

Type:
Psychic – Dragon

Height & weight:
7.5m/230.0kg

About: When Necrozma absorbs more light energy than it can contain, it takes on this form. Beams of light that have a strange effect on the natural world shoot out from Ultra Necrozma's entire body.

Nihilego

Ultra Beast

Type:
Rock – Poison

Height & weight:
1.2 m/55.5 kg

About: Nihilego, one of the mysterious Ultra Beasts, can apparently infest other beings and incite them to violence. Research is inconclusive as to whether this Pokémon can think for itself, but it sometimes exhibits the behaviour of a young girl.

Alolan Ninetales

Type:
Ice – Fairy

Height & weight:
1.1 m/19.9 kg

About: In its frosty coat, Ninetales creates ice droplets that can be used to shower over opponents. It's generally calm and collected, but if it becomes angry, it can freeze the offenders in their tracks.

Oranguru

Type:
Normal – Psychic

Height & weight:
1.5 m/76.0 kg

About: Extremely intelligent and somewhat particular, Oranguru can be a bad fit for Trainers who lack experience. In the wild, it spends most of its time in the jungle canopy, though it sometimes emerges in search of an intellectual challenge.

Oricorio *Baile Style*

Type:
Fire – Flying

Height & weight:
0.6 m/3.4 kg

About: Drinking red nectar gives Oricorio a fiery style when it dances. It's best to enjoy this beautiful performance from a distance, because its beating wings give off scorching flames.

Oricorio *Pa'u Style*

Type:
Psychic – Flying

Height & weight:
0.6 m/3.4 kg

About: Drinking pink nectar transforms Oricorio into a hypnotically swaying dancer. As its opponents watch, entranced, the swaying movement relaxes Oricorio's mind so it can build up psychic energy for attacks.

Oricorio *Pom-Pom Style*

Type:
Electric – Flying

Height & weight:
0.6 m/3.4 kg

About: Drinking yellow nectar makes Oricorio's dance style truly electric. The charge generated by the rubbing of its feathers allows it to land shocking punches in battle as it performs a cheerful dance.

Oricorio *Sensu Style*

Type:
Ghost – Flying

Height & weight:
0.6 m/3.4 kg

About: Drinking purple nectar inspires Oricorio to perform a dreamy and elegant dance. The spirits of the departed are drawn to this beautiful performance, and Oricorio channels their power into its attacks.

Palossand

Type:
Ghost – Ground

Height & weight:
1.3 m/250.0 kg

About: In order to evolve, this Pokémon took control of people playing in the sand to build up its body into a sand castle. Those who disappear can sometimes be found buried underneath Palossand, drained of their vitality.

Passimian

Type:
Fighting

Height & weight:
2.0 m/82.8 kg

About: Passimian are real team players – they learn from each other and work together for the benefit of the group. Each group, composed of about 20 Passimian, shares a remarkably strong bond.

Alolan Persian

Type:
Dark

Height & weight:
1.1 m/33.0 kg

About: Trainers in Alola adore Persian for its coat, which is very smooth and has a velvety texture. This Pokémon has developed a haughty attitude and prefers to fight dirty when it gets into battle.

Pheromosa

Ultra Beast

Type:
Bug – Fighting

Height & weight:
1.8 m/25.0 kg

About: Pheromosa, one of the mysterious Ultra Beasts, seems to be extremely wary of germs and won't touch anything willingly. Witnesses have seen it charging through the region at amazing speeds.

Pikipek

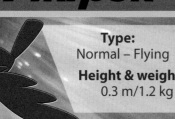

Type:
Normal – Flying

Height & weight:
0.3 m/1.2 kg

About: Pikipek can drill into the side of a tree at the rate of 16 pecks per second! It uses the resulting hole as a place to nest and to store berries – both for food and for use as projectiles.

Poipole

Ultra Beast

Type:
Poison

Height & weight:
0.6m/1.8kg

About: Poipole, one of the mysterious Ultra Beasts, is crowned with needles that spray a dangerous poison. This creature lives in another world, where it is popular enough that it could be a first partner.

Popplio

Type:
Water

Height & weight:
0.4 m/7.5 kg

About: Popplio uses the water balloons it blows from its nose as a weapon
in battle. It's a hard worker and puts in lots of practice creating and controlling these balloons.

Primarina

Type:
Water – Fairy

Height & weight:
1.8 m/44.0 kg

About: This Pokémon's singing voice is a delicate and powerful weapon, used to attack its foes and to control the water balloons it creates. Groups of Primarina teach these battle songs to the next generation.

Pyukumuku

Type:
Water
Height & weight:
0.3m/1.2 kg

About: Pyukumuku has a remarkable and revolting weapon in battle: it can spew out its innards to strike at its opponent. It's covered in a sticky slime that beachgoers use to soothe their skin after a sunburn.

Alolan Raichu

Type:
Electric – Psychic
Height & weight:
0.7 m/21.0 kg

About: Researchers speculate that Raichu looks different in the Alola region because of what it eats. It can "surf" on its own tail, standing on the flat surface and using psychic power to raise itself off the ground.

Alolan Raticate

Type:
Dark – Normal
Height & weight:
0.7 m/25.5 kg

About: Each Raticate leads a group of Rattata, and the groups regularly scuffle over food. This Pokémon is rather picky about what it eats, so a restaurant where a Raticate lives is likely to be a good one.

Alolan Rattata

Type:
Dark – Normal
Height & weight:
0.3 m/3.8 kg

About: Rattata sleep during the day and spend their nights searching for the best food to bring back to the Raticate who leads them. They use their strong teeth to gnaw their way into people's kitchens.

Ribombee

Type:
Bug – Fairy
Height & weight:
0.2 m/0.5 kg

About: Ribombee gathers up pollen and forms it into a variety of puffs with different effects. Some enhance battle skills and can be used as supplements, while others deliver excellent nutrition.

Rockruff

Type:
Rock
Height & weight:
0.5 m/9.2 kg

About: Rockruff has a long history of living in harmony with people. This friendly Pokémon is often recommended for Trainers just starting their journey, although it tends to develop a bit of a wild side as it grows.

Rowlett

Type:
Grass – Flying
Height & weight:
0.3 m/1.5 kg

About: During the day, Rowlett rests and generates energy via photosynthesis. In the night, it flies silently to sneak up on foes and launch a flurry of kicking attacks.

Salandit

Type:
Poison – Fire
Height & weight:
0.6 m/4.8 kg

About: Salandit gives off a toxic gas that causes dizziness and confusion when inhaled. It uses this gas to distract opponents before attacking. These Pokémon can often be found living on the slopes of volcanoes.

Alolan Sandshrew

Type:
Ice – Steel
Height & weight:
0.7 m/40.0 kg

About: Sandshrew lives high in the snowy mountains of Alola, where it has developed a shell of thick steel. It's very good at sliding across the ice – whether it does so under its own power or as part of a Sandshrew-sliding contest!

Alolan Sandslash

Type:
Ice – Steel
Height & weight:
1.2 m/55.0 kg

About: Sandslash is covered in spikes of tough steel, and in the cold mountains where it lives, each spike develops a thick coating of ice. A plume of snow flies up behind it as it dashes across the snowfield.

Sandygast

Type:
Ghost – Ground
Height & weight:
0.5 m/70.0 kg

About: A child created a mound of sand while playing on the beach, and it became a Sandygast. Putting your hand in its mouth is a sure way to fall prey to its mind control.

Shiinotic

Type:
Grass – Fairy
Height & weight:
1.0 m/11.5 kg

About: It's a bad idea to wander in Shiinotic's forest home at night. The strange, flickering lights given off by this Pokémon's spores can confuse travellers and cause them to lose their way.

Silvally

Type:
Normal

Height & weight:
2.3 m/100.5 kg

About: Learning to trust its Trainer caused this Pokémon to evolve and discard the mask that kept its power tightly controlled. Silvally can change its type in battle, making it a formidable opponent.

Solgaleo

Type:
Pyschic – Steel

Height & weight:
3.4 m/230.0 kg

About: Solgaleo's entire body radiates a bright light that can wipe away the darkness of night. This Legendary Pokémon apparently makes its home in another world, and it returns there when its third eye becomes active.

Stakataka

Ultra Beast

Type:
Rock – Steel

Height & weight:
5.5m/820.0kg

About: It's thought that Stakataka, one of the mysterious Ultra Beasts, is made up of several life-forms stacked on top of one another. This creature resembles a stone wall covered with markings that look like blue eyes.

Steenee

Type:
Grass

Height & weight:
0.7 m/8.2 kg

About: Lively and cheerful, Steenee often attracts a crowd of other Pokémon drawn to its energy and its lovely scent. Its sepals have evolved into a hard shell to protect its head and body from attackers.

Stufful

Type:
Normal – Fighting

Height & weight:
0.5 m/6.8 kg

About: Petting an unfamiliar Stufful is a bad idea, even though it's really cute – it dislikes being touched by anyone it doesn't consider a friend, and responds with a flailing of limbs that can knock over a strong fighter.

Tapu Bulu

Type:
Grass – Fairy

Height & weight:
1.9 m/45.5 kg

About: Tapu Bulu has a reputation for laziness – rather than battling directly, it commands vines to pin down its foes. The plants that grow abundantly in its wake give it energy. It's known as the Guardian of Ula'ula Island.

Tapu Fini

Type:
Water – Fairy

Height & weight:
1.3 m/21.2 kg

About: Tapu Fini can control and cleanse water, washing away impurities. When threatened, it summons a dense fog to confuse its enemies. This Pokémon draws energy from ocean currents. It's known as the Guardian of Poni Island.

Tapu Koko

Type:
Electric – Fairy

Height & weight:
1.8 m/20.5 kg

About: Somewhat lacking in attention span, Tapu Koko is quick to anger but just as quickly forgets why it's angry. Calling thunderclouds lets it store up lightning as energy. It's known as the Guardian of Melemele Island.

Tapu Lele

Type:
Psychic – Fairy

Height & weight:
1.2 m/18.6 kg

About: As Tapu Lele flutters through the air, people in search of good health gather up the glowing scales that fall from its body. It draws energy from the scent of flowers. It's known as the Guardian of Akala Island.

Togedemaru

Type:
Electric – Steel

Height & weight:
0.3 m/3.3 kg

About: Its back is covered with long, spiny fur that usually lies flat. But Togedemaru can bristle up the fur during battle for use as a weapon, or during storms to attract lightning, which it stores as electricity in its body.

Torracat

Type:
Fire

Height & weight:
0.7 m/25.0 kg

About: Torracat attacks with powerful punches from its front legs, which are strong enough to bend iron. When it spits flames, the fiery bell at its throat starts to ring.

Toucannon

Type:
Normal – Flying

Height & weight:
1.1 m/26.0 kg

About: The inside of Toucannon's beak gets very hot during a battle – over 90 degrees Celsius. The heat fuels its explosive seed-shooting and can also give opponents a serious scorching!

Toxapex

Type:
Poison – Water

Height & weight:
0.7 m/14.5 kg

About: It's a good thing Toxapex lives at the bottom of the ocean, because its poison is very dangerous. Those who fall prey to it can expect three very painful days before they recover, and the effects can linger.

Trumbeak

Type:
Normal – Flying

Height & weight:
0.6 m/14.8 kg

About: Trumbeak stores berry seeds in its beak to use as ammunition. It attacks opponents with a rapid-fire burst of seeds. Its beak is also very good at making lots of noise!

Tsareena

Type:
Grass

Height & weight:
1.2 m/21.4 kg

About: Beauty salons sometimes use images of the lovely Tsareena in their advertising. It can be a fierce fighter, using its long legs to deliver skilful kicks as it mocks its defeated opponent.

Turtonator

Type:
Fire – Dragon

Height & weight:
2.0 m/212.0 kg

About: Poisonous gases and flames spew from Turtonator's nostrils. Its shell is made of unstable material that might explode upon impact, so opponents are advised to aim for its stomach instead.

Type: Null

Type:
Normal

Height & weight:
1.9 m/120.5 kg

About: The synthetic Pokémon known as Type: Null wears a heavy mask to keep its power in check. Some fear that without the mask, it would lose control of its powers and go on a destructive rampage.

Vikavolt

Type:
Bug – Electric

Height & weight:
1.5 m/45.0 kg

About: Vikavolt uses its large jaws to focus the electricity it produces inside its body, then unleashes a powerful zap to stun its opponents. Flying-type Pokémon that once posed a threat are no match for its shocking attacks.

Alolan Vulpix

Type:
Ice

Height & weight:
0.6 m/9.9 kg

About: Vulpix in the Alola region were once known as "Keokeo", and some older folks still use that name. Its six tails can create a spray of ice crystals to cool itself off when it gets too hot.

Wimpod

Type:
Bug – Water

Height & weight:
0.5 m/12.0 kg

About: When the cowardly Wimpod flees from battle, it leaves a path swept clean by the passing of its many legs. It helps keep the beaches and seabeds clean, too, scavenging just about anything edible.

Wishiwashi *Solo Form*

Type:
Water

Height & weight:
0.2 m/0.3 kg

About: If a Wishiwashi looks like it's about to cry, watch out! The light that shines from its watering eyes draws the entire school, and they band together to fight off their opponent by sheer strength of numbers.

Wishiwashi *School Form*

Type:
Water

Height & weight:
8.2 m/78.6 kg

About: On its own, Wishiwashi is a feeble opponent, but when many Wishiwashi come together in a school, they are known as the demon of the sea. Their combined power is enough to scare away a Gyarados.

Xurkitree

Ultra Beast

Type:
Electric

Height & weight:
3.8 m/100.0 kg

About: Xurkitree, one of the mysterious Ultra Beasts, invaded an electric plant after it emerged from the Ultra Wormhole. Some suspect it absorbs electricity into its body to power the serious shocks it gives off.

Yungoos

Type:
Normal

Height & weight:
0.4 m/6.0 kg

About: Yungoos is always on the move during the day, looking for food – and it's not too picky about what it bites with its sharp teeth. When night comes, it immediately falls asleep no matter where it happens to be.

Island Challenge: Ula'ula Island

The island of Ula'ula in the south of the Alola region is where Ash takes his third island challenge. Try these Ula'ula tests yourself!

Colour in the shapes with a dot to reveal a Pokémon that's the master of disguise.

The Pokémon is:

Island Path

Help Ash and his Pokémon through the maze on Ula'ula to visit the island guardian, Tapu Bulu. Find **five** Pokémon altogether.

Crabominable

Vikavolt

Tapu Bulu

Mudsdale

Mimikyu

The answers are on page 69.

The Professor's Test

Think you'd make a top Trainer? Answer true or false to Professor Kukui's tricky questions to find out.

1 Necrozma is an Ultra Beast from another world.
True ☐ False ☐

2 Tapu Bulu is the Guardian of Akala Island.
True ☐ False ☐

3 The mysterious Ultra Beast, Poipole, can spray perfume from its needles.
True ☐ False ☐

4 Lusamine's team of Pokémon protectors is called the 'Ultra Guards'.
True ☐ False ☐

5 The Rock-type Pokémon, Stakataka, looks like a stone wall.
True ☐ False ☐

6 Bounsweet can only evolve once.
True ☐ False ☐

7 This Poké Ball is known as a Bee Ball.
True ☐ False ☐

8 A Z-Ring is needed if a Trainer is to perform Z-Moves.
True ☐ False ☐

The answers are on page 69.

Double Trouble

Lana has brought a Dewpider to show her friends at the Pokémon School. There are eight differences between these school scenes – can you spot them all?

1

2

Dewpider is a Water- and Bug-type Pokémon that evolves into Araquanid.

The answers are on page 69.

Twirling with a Bang

Ash is back on Melemele Island after successfully completing his third grand trial. Now he and his friends are relaxing at a fireworks festival, taking in some spectacular sights!

"Fireworks are the **best**!" Ash smiled, looking up at the sky, which was bursting with colour.

"**PIKA!**" Pikachu squeaked happily as a Pikachu-shaped firework exploded overhead. Popplio and Litten fireworks followed next.

"They are so cute!" Mallow laughed.

"Next up is the grand finale!" said Kiawe. But no one expected what was about to happen next …

From out of nowhere, a white ball decorated with colourful dots appeared. It bounced this way and that in the sky. Ash and his friends could hardly believe what they were seeing!

"It looks like a new, evolved form of fireworks!" Ash gasped.

"Maybe it's like an encore?" Lillie suggested.

The strange ball joined itself to a clown-shaped body that was waiting on a rock in the bay. Then it began performing some spectacular tricks to entertain the crowd!

"It's like magic!" said Lana.

Everyone took a step back, as the figure darted over the sea towards Ash and his friends. It stopped on some railings before suddenly making its head explode in a cloud of smoke, ***"Boom!"***

An incredible light display followed that was out of this world!

"It's like walking fireworks!" said Kiawe.

The figure gave a bow before skipping back over the waves and out of sight.

What Ash and his friends didn't see was that on a nearby island, another strange Pokémon had appeared. It had a spiked ball for a head and its long limbs looked like electrical cables.

At school the next day, everyone was talking about the creature – even the Pokémon!

"That fireworks dancer was so *amazing*!" smiled Ash. "I wonder what it was?"

"A *Pokémon*?" Mallow suggested. "Maybe even an *Ultra Beast*?"

The bell rang as usual, but today was no ordinary school day …

"*Ultra Guardians!* Quick, to the base!" said Professor Kukui, pressing a secret touchscreen underneath the classroom blackboard.

A hidden chamber opened and Ash and his friends entered. They quickly changed into their uniforms and their transformation into Ultra Guardians was complete!

Lusamine greeted them from a video screen.

"*Alola, Ultra Guardians!* We heard what happened last night at the fireworks," she began. "This being, after investigation, has been determined to be an *Ultra Beast*."

"So it really was a Pokémon," said Lillie.

"And an Ultra Beast at that!" added Mallow.

"We also detected an *Ultra Wormhole*, near the bay," Professor Burnet added.

"We have named the Ultra Beast '*Blacephalon*'," continued Lusamine.

Rotom Dex, began to update the new data. "Blacephalon. *The Fireworks Pokémon.* A Fire- and Ghost-type. Blacephalon surprises opponents by exploding its own head, then it *absorbs their energy*."

"It kept trying to surprise us … so it could absorb *our* energy!" Kiawe gasped.

Just then, the lights went out, the screen went blank and the base was plunged into darkness!

"Phew!" said Sophocles, when Clefable flicked the back-up switch to restore the power. Lusamine's Pokémon was in charge of taking care of the base.

"What **was** that?" said Ash, surprised.

The screen flashed on again. "We have found the cause," said Lusamine. "A powerful **Ultra Aura** has been detected on southern Route 3 on Melemele Island."

The Ultra Guardians had a new mission. They headed to board their Ride Pokémon – creatures that carry the Guardians around the region. One by one, they blasted off, leaving the base through a secret exit.

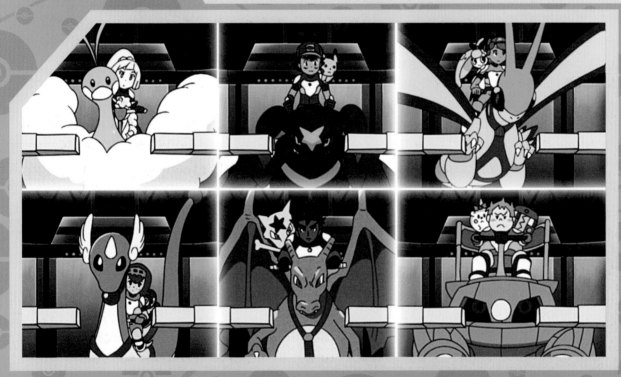

Ash and Pikachu were leading the way, when Pikachu's cheeks suddenly began to spark. The little Pokémon was picking up on something – electricity in the air!

"**Pika!**" Pikachu cried.

"Is it **Blacephalon**?" asked Mallow.

"Let's find out," Ash replied.

As they approached an electrical sub-station, the riders stopped and hovered in mid-air. There, before them, was another strange creature, its cable-like limbs draped over a pylon.

"It's not Blacephalon," said Kiawe.

"But Pikachu detected a powerful Ultra Aura?" said Sophocles, puzzled.

"Is it an **_Ultra Beast_**, too?" Mallow wondered.

The Guardians couldn't get any closer, as the creature began sending blasts of electricity straight at them! The suspected Ultra Beast was absorbing electricity directly from the power lines … and it didn't like being interrupted!

"Making an Ultra Catch isn't going to be easy," warned Kiawe.

Just then, a video call flashed up on Ash's glove.

"Situation update," Lusamine reported. "To our surprise, another Ultra Beast has appeared, just as we're studying Blacephalon."

"A new Ultra Wormhole must have opened from Blacephalon's explosions last night, which allowed the second Ultra Beast to appear," said Burnet.

Lusamine ordered the power to be shut down so the Ultra Beast couldn't feed off it. This would allow the Ultra Guardians to make their Ultra Catch … or so they thought!

But without power, the strange Ultra Beast sparked even more … now it was **_really angry_**!

"Sophocles! Let's distract it with some Electric-type moves!" Ash called.

"Got it!" Sophocles nodded.

Ash and Sophocles landed their Ride Pokémon, while the rest of the team took out their Beast Balls.

"If we all throw together one of them should make contact!" said Kiawe hopefully.

With the Guardians ready, Ash and Sophocles began their moves.

Pikachu opened with **Thunderbolt**, while Togedemaru used **Zing Zap**, blasting out electricity – it was sure to attract the Ultra Beast!

"Over here!" called Ash, trying to get the unknown Ultra Beast to follow them. "Come and get some yummy electricity!"

But before the creature could catch up, Blacephalon appeared again, and had become even more powerful.

The Guardians could only stand and watch as both Ultra Beasts began sparking wildly.

"What are they doing?" wondered Ash.

"Are they trying to compete with each other?" asked Mallow.

"Maybe now's the time for some serious Ultra Catching?" suggested Sophocles.

"Let's do it!" Ash agreed.

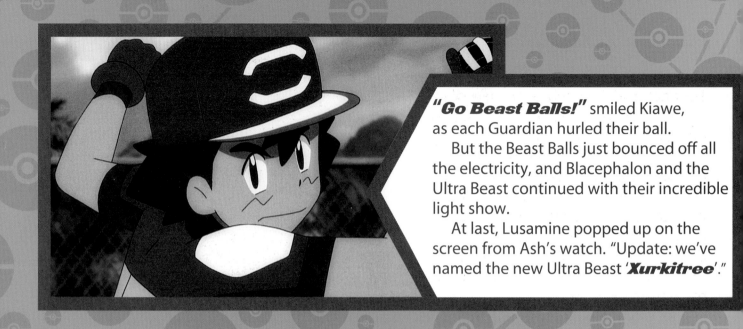

"Go Beast Balls!" smiled Kiawe, as each Guardian hurled their ball.

But the Beast Balls just bounced off all the electricity, and Blacephalon and the Ultra Beast continued with their incredible light show.

At last, Lusamine popped up on the screen from Ash's watch. "Update: we've named the new Ultra Beast '*Xurkitree*'."

"Xurkitree is the **Glowing Pokémon** … it unleashes powerful shocks using stored electricity. Be careful!" she warned.

Lillie was confused. "But what's going on?" she asked her mother.

"We think this is the first time that Blacephalon and Xurkitree have met," Lusamine replied. "And they're competing with all their might."

"Neither rival wants to lose!" added Ash.

The professors at the Aether Foundation were worried about what the Ultra Beasts were going to do next.

"We need to send them back to their world, as soon as we can," said Wicke.

The question was **how**? The Beast Balls hadn't worked.

Ash thought for a moment. "I've had an idea," he smiled. "If they want a show, they'll get one! We'll borrow some power from Pikachu and the other Pokémon, then combine our moves to make some super-flashy fireworks!"

Kiawe understood. "Yes! While our fireworks distract the Ultra Beasts . . ."

". . . we'll unleash a **Z-Move** that will end the battle for good!" Ash continued.

The Ultra Guardians assembled their Pokémon. Ash called Lycanroc, Kiawe his Turtonator, Mallow chose Steenee, Lillie her Alolan Vulpix and Sophocles brought Charjabug.

"All right! **Super Pokémon fireworks, GO!**" said Sophocles.

Next followed a series of moves that lit up the sky. It was a truly *electric* performance from the Pokémon! An enormous revolving firework sparkled and twirled above the Ultra Beasts, distracting them from their own light show. The perfect moment to throw in a Z-Move …

"Now, Lycanroc, let's do it!" Ash announced. "Full power – use **Splintered Stormshards!**"

Lycanroc launched hundreds of shards of rock towards the Ultra Beasts, which stopped them sparking!

While Blacephalon and Xurkitree were dazed and confused, Lillie and Mallow scored direct hits with their Beast Balls. This time, the Ultra Beasts were sucked inside.

"**We did it!**" smiled Ash.

"They've been **Ultra Caught!**" laughed Kiawe.

The next day, it was time for Blacephalon and Xurkitree to return to their home in Ultra Space. Ash and his friends gathered in the bay to see them blast back through the wormhole through which they had arrived. Thanks to the Ultra Guardians, Melemele Island was safe again.

Once again, the Ultra Guardians have successfully accomplished their mission! Now, although they don't know when another Ultra Beast may appear, one thing is certain: the peace of Alola depends on them!

Who's That Pokémon?

Which colourful creature was having a blast on Melemele Island? Put the picture back in order to find out!

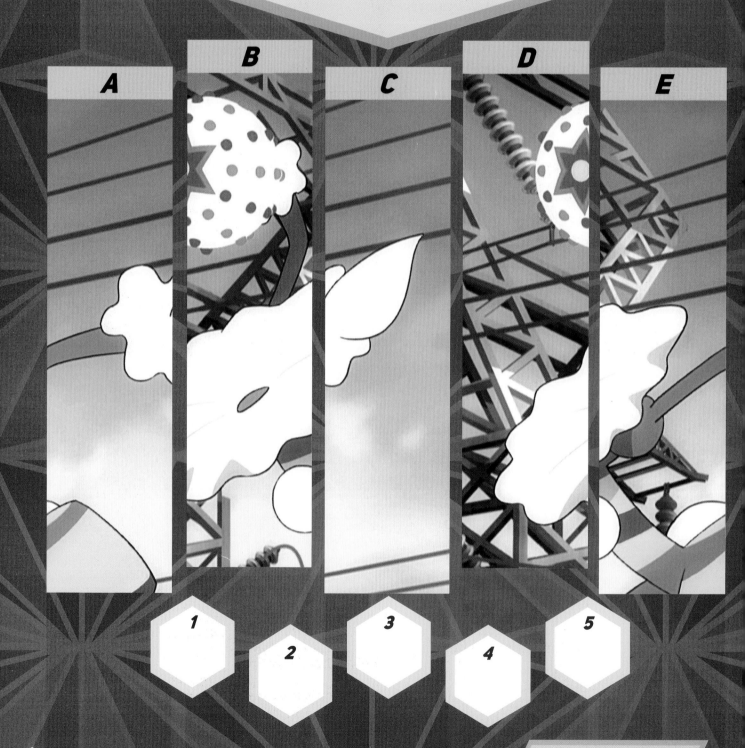

A   B   C   D   E

1   2   3   4   5

The answers are on page 69.

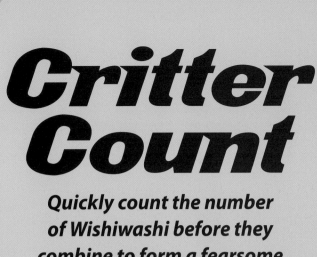

Critter Count

Quickly count the number of Wishiwashi before they combine to form a fearsome fiend of the sea!

In its School Form, *Wishiwashi* has the power to scare off a mighty Gyarados!

Wishiwashi

The answers are on page 69.

Making a Catch

Used to catch and store Pokémon, Poké Balls are important tools for any Trainer. Read the descriptions, then trace and colour the other half of these useful Poké Balls.

Every Trainer has stocks of the standard **Poké Ball** to catch Pokémon.

Master Balls are used to catch super-rare or Mythical Pokémon.

The special Poké Balls that are used to catch Ultra Beasts are called **Beast Balls**.

The yellow and black **Ultra Ball** has a higher catch rate than a standard Poké Ball.

Repeat Balls are useful for catching types of Pokémon that have been caught before.

Trainers choose the **Great Ball** because of its excellent catch rate.

The **Nest Ball** can be used to trap weaker Pokémon.

How to Draw ...
Poipole

Ash's Poipole is a playful Pokémon who loves making mischief with Pikachu!

1 Draw an egg shape, then a smiling mouth. Add two leaf-shaped eyes with a small spike above each eye.

2 Next, draw a zig-zag line above the eyes and draw a long diamond in the middle.

3 Draw the remaining details on the face, then add a small dome at the top of Poipole's head. You can rub out any sketch lines later on.

Poipole emerged from an Ultra Wormhole on Melemele Island.

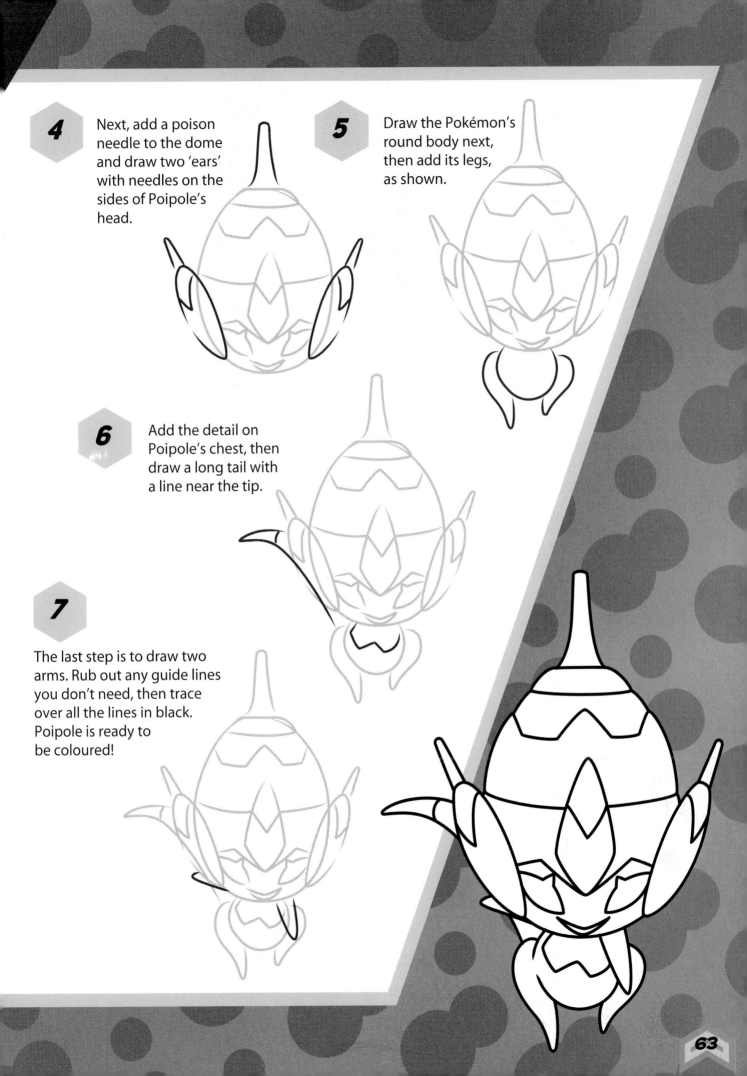

4 Next, add a poison needle to the dome and draw two 'ears' with needles on the sides of Poipole's head.

5 Draw the Pokémon's round body next, then add its legs, as shown.

6 Add the detail on Poipole's chest, then draw a long tail with a line near the tip.

7 The last step is to draw two arms. Rub out any guide lines you don't need, then trace over all the lines in black. Poipole is ready to be coloured!

The Ultra Beasts

Read the clues to work out which awesome Ultra Beasts appear in the crossword.

DOWN

2 The blade on this mini Grass- and Steel-type Pokémon is ultra sharp.

6 A cute-looking but poisonous Pokémon that is a friend to Pikachu.

7 A large, Poison- and Dragon-type that evolves from a smaller purple Pokémon.

9 A Bug- and Fighting-type, this Ultra Beast loves to flex its muscles.

ACROSS

1 Several life-forms stack up to form this stone-like beast.

3 This Electric Ultra Beast battled Blacephalon before being blasted back into Ultra Space.

4 This insect-like Pokémon's biggest fear is germs.

5 Known as the "Fireworks Pokémon", this creature is full of surprises.

8 Extremely dangerous, this sea-dwelling Ultra Beast has a venomous touch.

10 A heavyweight Ultra Beast with an appetite for destruction.

11 A mysterious metal Ultra Beast that can fly at incredible speeds.

The answers are on page 69.

Powerful Pokémon

Necrozma appears in different Formes when it absorbs the light of the Legendary Pokémon, Lunala or Solgaleo.

Add some colour to the picture to bring the beasts to life, then identify Necrozma's two new Formes.

Necrozma:

D _ _ _ M _ _ _ _

Necrozma:

D _ _ _ W _ _ _ _

The answers are on page 69.

Island Challenge: Poni Island

The fourth island that Ash and Pikachu travel to is Poni Island. Take on this tough trial of your own.

Find the Pokémon on the island and write down their coordinates. Ash and Pikachu are in square **C4**.

C 4

Ash & Pikachu

Ribombee

Kommo-o

Hakamo-o

Tapu Fini

Jangmo-o

7

6

5

4

3

2

1

A B C D E F G

The answers are on page 69.

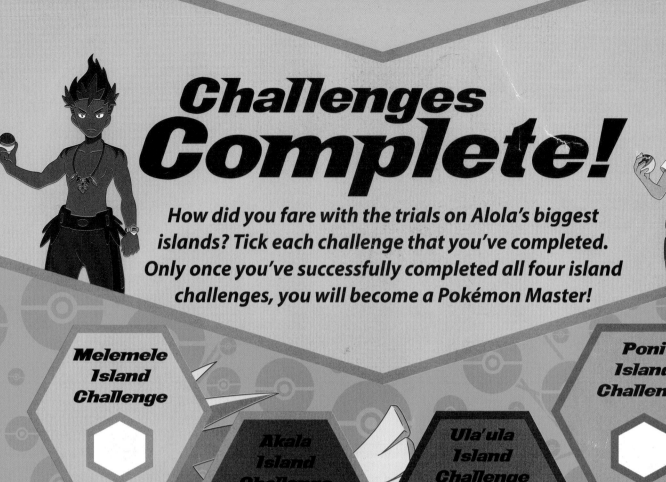

Challenges Complete!

How did you fare with the trials on Alola's biggest islands? Tick each challenge that you've completed. Only once you've successfully completed all four island challenges, you will become a Pokémon Master!

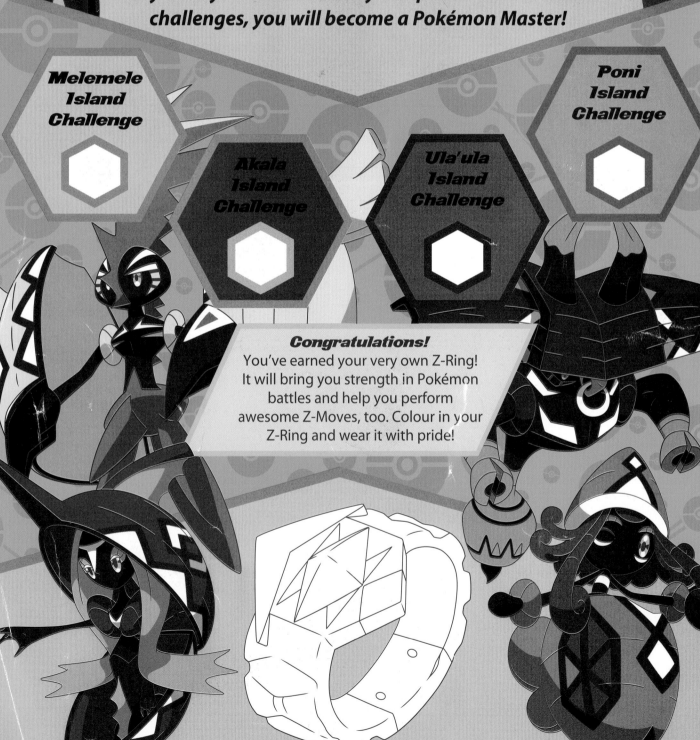

Melemele Island Challenge

Akala Island Challenge

Ula'ula Island Challenge

Poni Island Challenge

Congratulations!
You've earned your very own Z-Ring! It will bring you strength in Pokémon battles and help you perform awesome Z-Moves, too. Colour in your Z-Ring and wear it with pride!

Answers

Page 11
Special Stones

Mega Gengar is missing its Mega Stone.

Pages 12-13
Pokémon Partners

1. Tsareena = Mallow 2. Popplio = Lana, 3. Alolan Vulpix = Lillie 4. Pikachu = Ash 5. Turtonator = Kiawe

Page 14
Island Challenge: Melemele Island

Page 15
Forest Friend

The Pokémon is Tapu Koko.

Page 24
Island Challenge: Akala Island

```
U G N H S T U F F U L K M U W
Z T C G U J D R H W Q T S T R
W A L O L A N M A R O W A K B
R L A L M W C J K S T L N I Y
E J Q R B F M D M B H G D A N
S U G R T K E S Y C O J Y M T
M C T P D F O Y N Z R B G X E
B H Z I S I G I T G R A Q A L
P Y U K U M U K U L N C S M E
C U B A L U B I H G L C U L M
T N M C Z J S A W P E U W Q U
Y G P H K H K W L G E G M Z P
U O T U C Q J E U S H K R A T
Q O P W J Z B T W H P B H G T
A S K G O R A N G U R U Z U V
```

The Island Kahuna is OLIVIA.

Page 25
Hungry Pokémon

Pikipek – Sitrus Berry
Yungoos – Tamato Berry,
Oranguru – Oran Berry,
Alolan Marowak – Pecha Berry,
Pikachu is the Pokémon that will go hungry.

Page 26
Right Ring

Z-Ring B belongs to Ash.

Page 46
Island Challenge: Ula'ula Island

The Pokémon is Mimikyu.

Page 47
Island Path

Page 48
The Professor's Test

1. **False** – though it was once thought that this Legendary Pokémon was an Ultra Beast. 2. **False** – it is the Guardian of Ula'ula Island. 3. **False** – it can spray poison. 4. **False** – they are called the 'Ultra Guardians'. 5. **True**. 6. **False** – it can evolve twice – into Steenee and Tsareena. 7. **False** – it's an Ultra Ball. 8. **True**.

Page 49
Double Trouble

Page 58
Who's That Pokémon?

1. D, 2. B 3. E, 4. A, 5. C

Page 59
Critter Count

There are 22 Wishiwashi (Solo Form)

Page 64

```
        S T A K A T A K A
        A
        A
X U R K I T R E E
        T
        I
P H E R O M O S A
        A                N
B L A C E P H A L O N
        O         I
        N I H I L E G O
        P         E       A
    B   O                 D
    U   O                 A
G U Z Z L O R D          N
    Z                    E
    W                    L
    O
    E
    G E L E S T E E L A
```

Page 65
Powerful Pokémon

Necrozma: Dusk Mane
Necrozma: Dawn Wings

Pages 66-67
Island Challenge: Poni Island

The coordinates are:
Ribombee [F6] Hakamo-o [E3]
Kommo-o [B6]   Jangmo-o [C2]
Tapu Fini [F4]